THE OFFICIAL
CHESTERFIELD
FOOTBALL CLUB
QUIZ BOOK

THE OFFICIAL CHESTERFIELD FOOTBALL CLUB QUIZ BOOK

Compiled by Chris Cowlin

Foreword by Barrie Hubbard

APEX PUBLISHING LTD

Hardback first published in 2009 by
Apex Publishing Ltd
PO Box 7086, Clacton on Sea, Essex, CO15 5WN, England
www.apexpublishing.co.uk

British Library Cataloguing-in-Publication Data
A catalogue record for this book
is available from the British Library

ISBN HARDBACK: 1-906358-70-2   978-1-906358-70-9

Typeset in 10.5pt Chianti Bdlt Win95BT

Cover Design: Siobhan Smith

Printed and bound in Great Britain by the
MPG Books Group, Bodmin and King's Lynn

Author's Note:
Please can you contact me: **ChrisCowlin@btconnect.com** if you find any mistakes/errors in this book as I would like to put them right on any future reprints of this book. I would also like to hear from Chesterfield fans who have enjoyed the test! For more information on me and my books please look at: **www.ChrisCowlin.com**

This book is an official product of Chesterfield Football Club

We would like to dedicate this book to:

All the players and staff who have worked for the club during its history.

FOREWORD

As a lifelong supporter of Chesterfield Football Club, I feel honoured to be at the helm in our final season at Saltergate, which has been our home for 139 years.

For the 2010/11 season we will start life in a new purpose built stadium heralding a new era.

The Club has had many highs and lows during its history with the 1997 FA Cup journey ending in the semi final replay at Hillsborough, winning the Anglo Scottish Cup, beating Rangers on the way, being possibly the high points in our recent history, until now.

I have been lucky to be part of this great new era in the club's history and privileged to have been involved in our momentous move to our new home.

Hopefully, I have given you some good information in this foreword which will help in your enjoyment of this book, which is a must for all Chestefield fans (young and old), it will test your knowledge of Chesterfield players, past and present and the history of this great club.

Best wishes

Barrie Hubbard, Chesterfield Football Club (Chairman)

INTRODUCTION

I would first of all like to thank Barrie Hubbard for writing the foreword to this book. I am very grateful to him for his help and support on this project.

I would also like to thank everyone for their comments and reviews on this book (these can be found at the back of the book).

I would also like to thank Alan Stevenson and Tina Jenner for their help during the book's compilation.

I hope you enjoy this book. Hopefully it should bring back some wonderful memories!

I have given you a selection of easy, medium and hard questions so it will be fun for all the family!

In closing, I would like to thank all my friends and family for encouraging me to complete this book.

Chris Cowlin

Best wishes
Chris Cowlin

www.apexpublishing.co.uk

CLUB HISTORY

1. What is the name of the club's stadium?

2. In which two seasons did the club win the Division Four title?

3. What is the club's nickname?

4. Who is Chesterfield's record goalscorer with 162 League goals in 468 appearances between 1968 and 1986?

5. Which striker did Chesterfield buy from Watford for a club record of £250,000 in August 1998?

6. Against which team did Chesterfield achieve their record attendance of 30, 561 for an FA Cup match in February 1938?

7. True or false: the club have played in the top flight during their history?

8. Which Cup did the club win during the 1980/81 season?

9. In the history of Chesterfield FC, who has played the most games for the club, making a total of 658 appearances in the League, FA Cup and League Cup?

10. In which season during the 1990s did the club reach the semi-finals of the FA Cup?

MANAGERS – 1

*Match up the manager with the year
he took charge at Chesterfield*

11.	Harry Parkes	2007
12.	Arthur Cox	1919
13.	Jimmy McGuigan	2002
14.	Dave Rushbury	1973
15.	Teddy Davison	1967
16.	Frank Barlow	1922
17.	Nicky Law	1952
18.	Joe Shaw	1976
19.	Tom Callaghan	2000
20.	Lee Richardson	1980

JACK LESTER

21. What is Jack's middle name – Walter, Wayne or William?

22. From which club did Jack sign to join Chesterfield in 2007?

23. What squad number did Jack wear for Chesterfield during the 2008/09 season?

24. At which football club did Jack start his playing career?

25. Against which team did Jack score his first Chesterfield goal in an away defeat in the League Cup during August 2007?

26. Against which team did Jack score a League hat-trick in a 4-2 away win during November 2007?

27. True or false: Jack scored six goals in his first seven games playing for Chesterfield at The Recreation Ground?

28. Against which team did Jack score a brace in a 3-1 away League win on the opening day of the 2008/09 season?

29. Which Chesterfield manager signed Jack for the club in 2007?

30. In which year was Jack born – 1973, 1974 or 1975?

2008/2009

31.   In what position did Chesterfield finish in League 2?

32.   Who was in charge of the Spireites during this season?

33.   Which forward signed for Chesterfield from Macclesfield Town in January 2009?

34.   Which team did Chesterfield beat 6-1 away in October 2008?

35.   Who scored a hat-trick for the Spireites in a 5-1 home win against Aldershot Town in October 2008?

36.   How many of their 46 League matches did Chesterfield win this season?

37.   Who finished as the club's highest League scorer with 20 goals?

38.   Which team did Chesterfield beat 3-1 away from home in January 2009 in the club's first League win that year?

39.   Can you name the two Chesterfield scorers in the 2-2 home draw again Luton Town on Boxing Day 2008?

40.   Which striker scored a brace in a 2-1 home win against Exeter City in January 2009?

TOP LEAGUE APPEARANCES

Match up the player (one of the top ten appearance-makers in the club's history) with the number of appearances he made for Chesterfield in his career

41.	Gerry Sears	617
42.	Ron Powell	385 (5)
43.	Shaun O'Neill	413
44.	Albert Phelan	373 (20)
45.	Horace Wass	467 (3)
46.	Ernie Moss	471
47.	Jamie Hewitt	412
48.	Andy Kowalski	488 (18)
49.	David Blakey	437 (5)
50.	Albert Holmes	466 (3)

GORDON BANKS

51. In which year was Gordon born in Sheffield – 1935, 1936 or 1937?

52. For which club did Gordon sign when he left Chesterfield?

53. How many League appearances did Gordon make for Chesterfield in his career – 23, 83 or 143?

54. In what position did Gordon play during his playing days?

55. For which team did Gordon play between 1966 and 1972?

56. How many England caps did Gordon win during his playing career – 73, 83 or 93?

57. Which Chesterfield manager handed Gordon his club debut in the 1950s?

58. Following on from the previous question, against which Essex-based team did Gordon make his Chesterfield debut?

59. In which League were Chesterfield playing when Gordon made his only club appearances during the 1958/59 season?

60. True or false: Gordon once managed Chesterfield?

JIM BROWN

61. True or false: Jim scored a League goal for Chesterfield in his career?

62. How many League appearances did Jim make for Chesterfield during his career – 172, 182 or 192?

63. How many full international caps did Jim win for Scotland during his football career?

64. In which position did Jim play during his playing days?

65. From which team did Chesterfield sign Jim for a second spell at the club in 1983?

66. Which position at Chesterfield Football Club did Jim take in 1985?

67. From which Scottish team did Chesterfield sign Jim in 1972?

68. True or false: Jim played for the Scotland under-23 team whilst former Chesterfield favourite Alan Stevenson was in goal for the England under-23 side?

69. Which Chesterfield manager signed Jim when he joined the club for the first time in 1972?

70. How many League clean sheets did Jim keep whilst a Chesterfield player – 51, 52 or 53?

LEAGUE GOALSCORERS – 1

*Match up the player with the number of League goals
he scored for Chesterfield*

71.	Ernie Moss	26
72.	Dave Waller	28
73.	Tony Lormor	162
74.	Jamie Hewitt	62
75.	Bob Newton	47
76.	Ivan Hollett	40
77.	Phil Walker	53
78.	Alan Birch	26
79.	Glynn Hurst	29
80.	Lee Turnbull	34

WHERE DID THEY COME FROM? – 1

Match up the player with the club he left to join Chesterfield

81.	David Reeves	Peterborough United
82.	Ricky Green	Watford
83.	Phil Bonnyman	Walsall
84.	Paul Holland	Preston North End
85.	Geoff Salmons	Scunthorpe United
86.	Steve Wilkinson	Torquay United
87.	Bill Green	Leicester City
88.	John Turner	Preston North End
89.	Alan Birch	Sheffield United
90.	Jason Lee	Carlisle United

MANAGERS – 2

Match up the manager with the year he took charge at Chesterfield

91.	Roy McFarland	1988
92.	John Duncan (1st spell)	1945
93.	Bill Harvey	1991
94.	Paul Hart	1962
95.	Bob Brocklebank	2003
96.	Chris McMenemy	1993
97.	Tony McShane	1980
98.	Bob Marshall	1983
99.	John Duncan (2nd spell)	1932
100.	Frank Barlow	1949

CHESTERFIELD V. MANSFIELD TOWN

101. What was the score when Chesterfield beat Mansfield in the FA Cup 1st round in November 2008?

102. Following on from the previous question, which forward scored a brace in the game for Chesterfield?

103. True or false: the teams did not meet in any competition during the 1940s?

104. Which Chesterfield midfielder scored a brace in a 4-0 League home win over Mansfield Town in September 2000?

105. Apart from the League, in which other competition did the sides meet during the 1971/72 season?

106. Which Chesterfield player scored a brace in a 5-2 win in the play-off semi-final, 2nd leg, in May 1995?

107. In which year did the two clubs first meet in the League, in a 3-0 away win for Chesterfield – 1931, 1933 or 1935?

108. How many of the 10 League meetings between the two clubs did Chesterfield win during the 1980s?

109. Which midfielder score Chesterfield's two goals in a 2-1 away League win in January 1994?

110. True or false: Chesterfield won both League meetings during the 2007/08 season?

DEBUTS

111. Who scored four minutes into his debut against Brentford in February 2008 in a 1-0 home win?

112. Who was the last Spireites player to make a debut during 2008, in a 5-1 League win against Aldershot Town in October?

113. How many Chesterfield players made their debuts in the League during the 2004/05 season?

114. Who scored on his debut in a 4-2 away defeat to Grimsby Town in the League in February 2008?

115. How many Chesterfield players made their debuts in the League during the 1973/74 season?

116. True or false: Paul Shaw scored on his debut against Bournemouth in August 2006 in a 3-0 League away win?

117. Who scored on his debut in a 4-2 away defeat to Hereford United in the League in January 1976?

118. True or false: six Chesterfield players made their debuts against York City in a 4-1 home League win during August 2000?

119. Who scored Chesterfield's goal on his debut in a 1-1 home draw in December 1990 against Gillingham?

120. Who made his debut against Bradford City in a 2-0 home defeat in May 2009?

RON POWELL

121. How many League appearances did Ron make for Chesterfield in his career – 371, 471 or 571?

122. From which club did Ron sign when he joined Chesterfield?

123. In what year did Ron sign for Chesterfield?

124. What did Ron do after retiring from playing football?

125. In what position did Ron play during his playing days?

126. How many clean sheets in League competitions did Ron keep during his Chesterfield career – 113, 123 or 133?

127. In what year did Ron make his last League appearance for Chesterfield?

128. True or false: Ron once scored a League goal for Chesterfield?

129. Against which team did Ron make his Chesterfield League debut, in a 4-1 home win?

130. How many League goals did Ron concede during his time at Chesterfield – 734, 744 or 754?

NATIONALITIES

Match up the player with his nationality

131.	Gregor Robertson	English
132.	Kevin Austin	Irish
133.	Robert Page	English
134.	Alan Goodall	Scottish
135.	Caleb Folan	Scottish
136.	Jamie Lowry	Australian
137.	Derek Niven	Welsh
138.	Lewis Montrose	Scottish
139.	Martin Gritton	English
140.	Aaron Downes	Trinidad & Tobago

1960s

141.   In which League position in Division Four did Chesterfield finish during 1964/65 – 10th, 12th or 14th?

142.   Which Chesterfield striker scored twice on his debut in a 3-0 home League win against Halifax Town in September 1960?

143.   Which Chesterfield goalkeeper played in every League match during the 1967/68 season?

144.   Which centre half was the only ever-present Chesterfield player in the League during the 1961/62 season?

145.   In which League position in Division Four did Chesterfield finish during 1963/64 – 16th, 17th or 18th?

146.   Who managed Chesterfield between 1962 and 1967?

147.   Which opponents visited Chesterfield when the club recorded an attendance of 16,603 in a Division Four match in December 1967?

148.   In which League position in Division Four did Chesterfield finish during 1967/68 – 6th, 7th or 8th?

149.   Name the two Chesterfield players who scored hat-tricks for the club during the 1966/67 season.

150.   How many Chesterfield players made their League debut during the 1966/67 season – 8, 9 or 10?

JOHN SHERIDAN

151. In what year was John appointed as Chesterfield manager?

152. Which club did John manage before Chesterfield?

153. In what position did John play during his playing days?

154. What is John's middle name – Jamie, Joseph or John?

155. How many international goals did John score for the Republic of Ireland in his 34 full international caps?

156. True or false: John played for Chesterfield during his playing career?

157. In which year was John born – 1962, 1964 or 1966?

158. Whom did John appoint as his assistant manager when he took charge at Chesterfield?

159. Against which team did John score the only, winning goal in the 1991 League Cup while playing for Sheffield Wednesday?

160. For which Yorkshire-based team did John play between 1982 and 1989?

ALBERT HOLMES

161. In what year did Albert join Chesterfield on a semi-professional basis, signing professional terms a year later?

162. Albert occasionally played as a forward, but in what position did he mainly play during his playing days?

163. Against which team did Albert score for Chesterfield in 1974, potting a strike from 20 yards?

164. In which year did Albert leave Saltergate – 1972, 1973 or 1974?

165. Following on from the previous question, which Chesterfield manager released Albert from the club?

166. What is the name of Albert's son, who was also a professional footballer and played for Doncaster, Torquay, Birmingham and Everton?

167. How many League appearances did Albert make while at Chesterfield – 470, 480 or 490?

168. True or false: Albert was a full England international, winning four caps for his country?

169. How many League goals did Albert score for Chesterfield during his career – 1, 10 or 11?

170. What profession did Albert take up after retiring from playing professional football?

GOALSCORING DEBUTANTS

Match up the player with the team he scored against on his League debut

171. **Martin Gritton**

Gillingham (August 1993), 2-0 away win

172. **Phil Cliff**

Rochdale (November 1972), 2-1 away win

173. **Bill Curry**

York City (August 2000), 4-1 home win

174. **Mark Innes**

Chester City (January 2009), 3-1 away win

175. **Walter Ponting**

Bury (October 1932), 3-1 home defeat

176. **Frank Large**

Barrow (August 1922), 2-1 home win

177. **Mark Jules**

Rochdale (February 1971), 1-1 home draw

178. **Sean Parrish**

Barnsley (January 1968), 3-2 home defeat

179. **Norman Whitfield**

Brighton & Hove Albion (December 2001), 2-2 away draw

180. **Colin Cook**

Southampton (August 1936), 3-2 away defeat

ERNIE MOSS

181. In which year was Ernie born in Chesterfield – 1949, 1950 or 1951?

182. In what position did Ernie play during his playing days?

183. How many playing spells did Ernie have at Chesterfield?

184. True or false: Ernie managed Chesterfield during his managerial career?

185. Against which team did Ernie make his Chesterfield debut in October 1968?

186. How many League goals did Ernie score during his Chesterfield career – 102, 162 or 202?

187. Against which team did Ernie play in his testimonial in 1986?

188. True or false: Ernie never took a penalty for Chesterfield in a League match?

189. How many League appearances did Ernie make for Chesterfield – 468, 488 or 508?

190. True or false: Ernie holds the record for being the highest League goalscorer in the club's history?

2006/2007

191. Which team did Chesterfield beat 3-0 away from home on the opening day of the League season?

192. Which two Chesterfield players scored a brace in a 5-1 home League win in August 2006?

193. In what position in the League did Chesterfield finish during this season?

194. For which club did Carl Muggleton sign when he left Chesterfield before this season, during July 2006?

195. Which two Chesterfield players appeared in 45 out of the club's 46 League matches during this season?

196. Which Chesterfield player scored a brace in a 3-0 home win against Bradford City in April 2007?

197. Which team did Chesterfield beat 3-0 at home in February 2007?

198. Which Chesterfield midfielder scored the winning goal in a 2-1 home League win against Rotherham United in September 2006?

199. Which midfielder did Chesterfield sign from Torquay United in January 2007?

200. How many of their 46 League matches did Chesterfield win during the season – 11, 12 or 13?

MANAGERS – LEAGUE WINS

*Match up the manager with the number of times he won
League games throughout his time as Chesterfield manager*

201. Lee Richardson   68 wins out of
                                 180 games

202. Dave Rushbury   101 wins out of
                                 202 games

203. Chris McMenemy   34 wins out of
                                 76 games

204. Harry Parkes   34 wins out of
                                 100 games

205. Alec Campbell   46 wins out of
                                 142 games

206. Arthur Cox   33 wins out of
                                 93 games

207. Duggie Livingstone   37 wins out of
                                 101 games

208. Bob Marshall   19 wins out of
                                 66 games

209. Paul Hart   4 wins out of
                                 15 games

210. Nicky Law   59 wins out of
                                 182 games

THE FA CUP

211. Can you name the team that Chesterfield Town played in their first ever FA Cup match in October 1892?

212. Which East Anglian team knocked Chesterfield out of the 3rd round during the 2008/09 competition?

213. Which team knocked out The Spireites in the semi-final in April 1997?

214. Which team knocked out The Spireites in the 4th round replay in February 1954?

215. True or false: Chesterfield played replays in the 1st, 2nd and 3rd rounds during the 1980/81 competition?

216. By what scoreline did Chesterfield beat Wrexham in the quarter-finals in March 1997?

217. True or false: Chesterfield won this competition in 1981?

218. Which club beat Chesterfield 6-0 away from home in the 3rd round in January 1949?

219. Which round of the competition did Chesterfield reach during the 1937/38 season?

220. True or false: Chesterfield were knocked out of the competition in the 1st round in every season from 2002/03 to 2007/08?

JOHN DUNCAN

221. True or false: John played for Chesterfield during his playing days?

222. In what position did John play during his playing days?

223. What is John's middle name – Peterson, Parsons or Pearson?

224. John took over from which manager when he took charge at Chesterfield in 1983?

225. In which year was John born – 1949, 1951 or 1953?

226. At the end of which season did John guide Chesterfield to promotion to Division 2 after winning the play-offs?

227. During the 1984/85 season John guided Chesterfield to winning what?

228. At which club did John start his managerial career in the early 1980s?

229. At which Scottish club did John start his football career in the late 1960s?

230. Which manager did John succeed when he took charge for a second time at Chesterfield in 1993?

THE STADIUM

231.   If you had purchased an adult season ticket in the
       family stand during July 2009 how much would you
       have paid - £240, £340 or £440?

232.   What is the postcode of the club's stadium?

233.   What is the record attendance for a Chesterfield match
       at the stadium, played in 1949 – 10,986, 20,986 or
       30,986?

234.   Following on from the previous question, which team
       were Chesterfield playing on that day?

235.   True or false: the club's stadium acted as Wembley
       Stadium, the Baseball Ground, Carrow Road, and
       Bloomfield Road in the 2009 film The Damned United?

236.   What is the size of the club's pitch - 113 x 71 yards,
       123 x 73 yards or 133 x 75 yards?

237.   Can you name the stadium's four stands?

238.   What is the stadium's capacity – 7,504, 8,504 or
       9,504?

239.   In what year was the stadium built and opened?

240.   If you were phoning the club's stadium what area code
       would you use?

LEGENDS – 1

*Rearrange the letters to reveal the name of
a Chesterfield legend*

241.   IYMMJ SOOKNOC

242.   VIKNE VESDIA

243.   MIJ NWBOR

244.   SACRUM BENDO

245.   YAGR LAMBYEL

246.   ALNA CRBHI

247.   ADEV LAWREL

248.   REACHO SAWS

249.   ELE GRROSE

250.   ADIDV ESEVER

GOALKEEPERS' CLEAN SHEETS

251. How many clean sheets did Mike Pollitt make in his 46 League appearances for Chesterfield?

252. Which goalkeeper made his Chesterfield debut in the 1984/85 season and had 50 clean sheets in 141 League matches for the club?

253. How many clean sheets did Nathan Abbey make in his 46 League appearances for Chesterfield?

254. Which goalkeeper made 59 League clean sheets for Chesterfield in his 186 appearances, having made his debut in the 1933/34 season?

255. Which goalkeeper made his Chesterfield League debut in 1977/78 and kept 6 clean sheets in 16 League games for the club?

256. Which goalkeeper, while on loan, kept 2 clean sheets in 2 League games during 1996/97?

257. Mick Leonard made 51 League clean sheets in his Chesterfield career, but how many League goals did he concede while playing in 176 games for the club – 224, 244 or 264?

258. How many League clean sheets did Tommy Lee keep during the 2008/09 season?

259. Which goalkeeper made his debut in the 1995/96 season and had 55 clean sheets in 149 League matches?

260. Which goalkeeper made a club record of 113 League clean sheets for Chesterfield in his 471 appearances?

2004/2005

261. In what position in League 1 did Chesterfield finish this season?

262. Which midfielder finished as the club's highest League scorer with 8 goals?

263. Which club did Chesterfield beat 3-1 away from home on the opening day of the League season?

264. Following on from the previous question, which player scored a brace in the game?

265. With which side did Chesterfield share a 2-2 League draw on Boxing Day 2004?

266. Which Chesterfield player made his debut for the club during March 2005 in a 2-2 away draw against Brentford?

267. Which Chesterfield midfielder scored a hat-trick in a 5-1 home League win against Aldershot in October 2008?

268. True or false: Chesterfield failed to score a League goal in their last five League matches of the season?

269. Against which team did Chesterfield record their first League win of 2005, beating them 3-1 away on 17 January 2009?

270. How many of their 46 League games did Chesterfield win – 12, 14 or 16?

DAVE BLAKEY

271.   How many League goals did Dave score during his
        Chesterfield career – 10, 20 or 30?

272.   In what year did Dave make his Chesterfield League
        debut?

273.   Against which team did Dave make his Chesterfield
        League debut, in a 0-0 away draw in Division 2?

274.   In what position did Dave play during his playing
        days?

275.   Dave made 35 FA Cup appearances for Chesterfield
        during his club career, but how many League Cup
        appearances did his make - 6, 8 or 10?

276.   In what year did Dave make his final Chesterfield
        appearance?

277.   True or false: Dave played League games for
        Chesterfield in Division 2, Division 3, Division 3 North
        and Division 4?

278.   What club record does Dave hold at Chesterfield?

279.   Why was Dave sent off after only 13 minutes while
        playing for Chesterfield against Bradford City in 1958?

280.   How many League appearances did Dave make during
        in his Chesterfield career – 607, 617 or 627?

WHO AM I?

281. I managed the club between 1945 and 1949.

282. I scored two Chesterfield League hat-tricks during the 1958/59 season, both against Southend United, one at home and the other away.

283. I made my Chesterfield League debut during the 1952/53 season and scored 98 League goals in 250 appearances for the club.

284. I left my position as Oldham Athletic's manager to take charge of The Spireites in the summer of 2009.

285. I made my Chesterfield League debut during the 1953/54 season and scored 58 League goals in 176 appearances for the club.

286. Born in 1978, I am a striker and signed from Macclesfield Town for Chesterfield in January 2009, scoring 4 League goals for the club in my first season.

287. I made my Chesterfield League debut during the 1930/31 season and scored 39 League goals in 64 appearances for the club.

288. Born in 1984, I am a Scottish defender and arrived at Chesterfield from Rotherham on a free transfer in July 2007.

289. I made my Chesterfield League debut during the 1990/91 season and scored 26 League goals in 87 appearances for the club.

290. Born in 1983, I am a defender and signed for Chesterfield from Gretna in July 2008.

NICKY LAW

291. In what year was Nicky born in Greenwich – 1959, 1960 or 1961?

292. At which London club did Nicky start his professional football career in 1979, signing as an apprentice?

293. From which club did Nicky sign when he joined Chesterfield in 1993?

294. In what year did Nicky leave Chesterfield to join Hereford United?

295. Nicky took over from which Chesterfield manager in 2000?

296. As club manager Nicky guided Chesterfield to what during the 2000/01 season?

297. True or false: Nicky was a striker during his playing days?

298. How many League goals did Nicky score for Chesterfield during his club career – 11, 17 or 23?

299. True or false: Nicky was on the losing side when he made his Chesterfield debut, in a 4-1 away defeat?

300. How many League appearances did Nicky make during his Chesterfield career – 117, 127 or 137?

PLAYER POSITIONS

Match up the player with his playing position

301.	Billy Kidd	Goalkeeper
302.	Cliff Carr	Goalkeeper
303.	Gerry Sears	Right back
304.	Ron Powell	Forward
305.	Mark Williams	Left back
306.	Tom Curtis	Left back
307.	Stan Milburn	Midfielder
308.	Freddie Capel	Centre back
309.	Arnold Birch	Right back
310.	Ernie Moss	Left back

2007/2008

311. How many players made their League debuts during this season?

312. Which Chesterfield manager was in charge of the club for his first full season in 2007/08?

313. In what position did Chesterfield finish in League 2?

314. How many League goals did Jack Lester score for Chesterfield during this season, making 35 starts and 1 substitute appearance?

315. Against which team did Chesterfield record their first win of the season, in their third League match of 2007/08, winning 3-2 away in August 2007?

316. Name the two substitutes that scored in a 4-2 away defeat to Grimsby Town in February 2008?

317. True or false: three Chesterfield players were ever present during this season?

318. How many League goals did Jamie Ward score for Chesterfield during this season in his 27 starts and 8 substitute appearances?

319. Jack Lester scored the club's only hat-trick of the season in a 4-2 League away win against which team?

320. How many of their 46 League matches did Chesterfield win – 19, 23 or 27?

HAT-TRICK HEROES

321. Who scored a Chesterfield League hat-trick in a 5-1 home win during 2008/09 against Aldershot Town?

322. How many hat-tricks did Jimmy Cookson score for The Spireites during the 1925/26 season?

323. What was the final score when Rod Fern achieved a hat-trick for The Spireites against Bury at home during 1976/77?

324. Who scored a hat-trick of penalties against Sheffield Wednesday in a 4-2 home win during 1946/47?

325. How many competitive hat-tricks, a club record, did Jimmy Cookson score for Chesterfield in his career?

326. In which competition did Kevin Davies score a hat-trick for The Spireites against Bolton Wanderers during 1996/97?

327. Who scored a Chesterfield League hat-trick in a 4-2 home win against Cambridge United during 1999/2000?

328. True or false: three different players scored hat-tricks for The Spireites in League competition during the 2005/06 season?

329. Against which club did Martin Wright score a League Cup hat-trick in a 5-0 home win during the 1971/72 season?

330. Which player scored a hat-trick in a 4-1 League home win against Macclesfield Town during the 2000/2001 season?

CHESTERFIELD V. NOTTINGHAM FOREST

331. True or false: Chesterfield won the clubs' first ever meeting in October 1906?

332. In which competition did the sides meet in a 1-0 Chesterfield home win in February 1997?

333. Following on from the previous question, who scored the club's only goal?

334. Which Chesterfield defender scored in the club's 2-1 home defeat in February 2007?

335. In which division did the sides meet during the 1948/49 season?

336. What was the score when the sides met in December 1938 in Division 2 – 5-1 to Chesterfield, 6-1 to Chesterfield or 7-1 to Chesterfield?

337. In which competition have these sides never met – The League Cup, The FA Cup or League 1?

338. True or false: Chesterfield beat Forest both at home and away in the League during 1948/49?

339. True or false: the sides met in League competition during the 1960s, 1970s and 1980s?

340. Which Chesterfield defender scored in the club's 3-1 home League defeat during April 2006?

ROY McFARLAND

341. In what year was Roy appointed as Chesterfield manager?

342. For how many League games did Roy manage Chesterfield – 175, 195 or 215?

343. Following on from the previous question, how many League games did the club win under Roy's management – 40, 50 or 60?

344. For how many games (in all competitions) was Roy in charge at Chesterfield before the club achieved a win, a 2-1 home victory over Macclesfield in the LDV Vans Trophy?

345. How many full England caps did Roy win during his playing career – 18, 28 or 38?

346. In what position did Roy play during his playing days?

347. What is Roy's middle name – Leslie, Leon or Lee?

348. Which club did Roy manage between 1996 and 2001?

349. In what year did Roy leave Chesterfield as club manager?

350. Following on from the previous question, who took over as Chesterfield manager when Roy left the club?

2002/2003

351. Who finished as Chesterfield's top League scorer with eight goals?

352. How many players made their League debuts during this season – 12, 13 or 14?

353. In what position did Chesterfield finish in the League?

354. Which midfielder did Chesterfield sign on a permanent basis from Middlesbrough in March 2003?

355. Who started this season as Chesterfield manager?

356. Which striker scored a brace in a 4-0 League home win in August 2002?

357. Which team did Chesterfield beat 1-0 away on Boxing Day 2002?

358. What was the score when Chesterfield played Wycombe Wanderers in the League at home in March 2003?

359. True or false: no Chesterfield player scored a League hat-trick during this season?

360. How many of their 46 League matches did Chesterfield win – 14, 16 or 18?

LOAN PLAYERS

Match up the player with the club from which he joined Chesterfield on loan (and the season)

361.	Jamie O'Hara	**Leyton Orient (1996/97)**
362.	Ian Seddon	**Tottenham Hotspur (2006/07)**
363.	John Roberts	**Peterborough United (1987/88)**
364.	Peter Hartley	**Charleroi (1986/87)**
365.	Jordan Fowler	**Birmingham City (2001/02)**
366.	Carl Airey	**Tottenham Hotspur (2005/06)**
367.	Charlie Daniels	**Arsenal (2004/05)**
368.	David Hanson	**Chester City (1975/76)**
369.	Graham Hyde	**Blackburn Rovers (1967/68)**
370.	Steve Phillips	**Sunderland (2007/08)**

MATCH THE YEAR

Match up the event with the year in which it happened

371. Ambrose Brown scored five goals
     for Chesterfield against Mansfield Town   **1970**

372. Chesterfield beat Scunthorpe United
     5-0 in the League   **1957**

373. The club were Division 3
     North Champions   **1938**

374. The club reached the FA Cup semi-finals   **1947**

375. Chesterfield beat Mansfield Town
     5-0 in the League   **1935**

376. The club reached their highest
     Football League position:
     4th in Division 2   **1996**

377. The club recorded their record
     attendance of 30,561 v. Tottenham
     Hotspur in the FA Cup   **1972**

378. The club were Division 3
     play-off winners   **1931**

379. The club were Division 4 Champions   **1971**

380. Burnley beat Chesterfield
     7-0 in the FA Cup   **1997**

LEAGUE POSITIONS – 1

*Match up the season with the club's finishing
position in the League*

381.	1960/61	20th in Division 4
382.	1961/62	7th in Division 4
383.	1962/63	20th in Division 4
384.	1963/64	1st in Division 4
385.	1964/65	15th in Division 4
386.	1965/66	12th in Division 4
387.	1966/67	24th in Division 3
388.	1967/68	16th in Division 4
389.	1968/69	19th in Division 4
390.	1969/70	15th in Division 4

THE LEAGUE CUP

391. Who were Chesterfield's opponents in the first ever League Cup match in the club's history, in a 1-0 home win during November 1960?

392. Which London club knocked Chesterfield out of the competition in the 4th round during 2006/07?

393. In what season during the 1960s did the club reach the 4th round?

394. Which club did Chesterfield beat 5-0 in a 1st round replay in August 1972?

395. With which top-flight side did Chesterfield share a 4-4 away draw in the League Cup 2nd round, 2nd leg, in September 1992?

396. Which team did Chesterfield play in the 1st round in the 1970/71, 1971/72 and 1973/74 seasons?

397. Which Midlands-based club knocked The Spireites out of the competition in September 1971?

398. Name the player who scored the first ever goal for Chesterfield in this competition.

399. Which London club knocked Chesterfield out of the competition in round 2 during the 2002/03 season?

400. True or false: Chesterfield have won this competition once in their history?

TRANSFERS

Match up the player with his transfer fee

401.	Joe Ball	**Notts County paid Chesterfield £1,000**
402.	Harry Roberts	**West Bromwich Albion paid Chesterfield £2,500**
403.	Willis Edwards	**Chesterfield paid Bury £400**
404.	Allan Sliman	**Chesterfield paid Leicester City £35,000**
405.	Bill Green	**Birmingham City paid Chesterfield £10,600**
406.	Paul Holland	**Everton paid Chesterfield £100**
407.	Joe Cooper	**Leeds United paid Chesterfield £1,500**
408.	Ellis Gee	**Chesterfield paid Sheffield United £150,000**
409.	Jimmy Cookson	**Chesterfield paid Bristol City £1,500**
410.	Geoff Salmons	**Chesterfield paid Peterborough United £40,000**

CHESTERFIELD V. SHEFFIELD WEDNESDAY

411. True or false: the clubs didn't meet in any competition during the 1980s and 1990s?

412. Which midfielder scored Chesterfield's equaliser in the 55th minute to make the score 2-2 at Hillsborough in October 2004?

413. What was the score when Sheffield Wednesday visited Chesterfield in March 2004 in the League?

414. Following on from the previous question, which Chesterfield forward scored a brace in the game?

415. True or false: the teams played each other in the League Cup during the 2005/06 season?

416. Which team won the first League meeting between the two sides in September 1899?

417. In which 1970s season did Chesterfield beat Wednesday both at home and away in League competition?

418. What was the score when the teams met in the League at Hillsborough in December 2003?

419. Who scored a 90th-minute goal for Chesterfield in their 3-1 home defeat in February 2005 in League 1?

420. In which 1940s season did Chesterfield beat Wednesday both at home and away in League competition?

WHERE DID THEY GO? – 1

Match up the player with the club he joined
on leaving Chesterfield

421.	Kevin Davies	Wolves
422.	Alan Birch	Middlesbrough
423.	Jim Brown	West Bromwich Albion
424.	Alan Stevenson	Newcastle United
425.	Gordon Dale	Huddersfield Town
426.	Harry Roberts	Southampton
427.	Billy Whitaker	Burnley
428.	Harry Clifton	Sheffield United
429.	Albert Malam	Birmingham City
430.	Jimmy Cookson	Portsmouth

1990s

431. Which right back played in every League match for Chesterfield during the 1991/92 season?

432. Which Chesterfield player scored on his League debut against Gillingham in a 2-0 away win in August 1993?

433. Who scored a hat-trick for Chesterfield in a Associate Members Cup match against Burnley during the 1992/93 season?

434. Who took over as Chesterfield manager in January 1991?

435. In which season during the 1990s did the club finish 3rd in Division 3?

436. Which Chesterfield player came on as a substitute on his League debut and scored in a 1-0 home win against Crewe in October 1996?

437. How much was a match-day programme at Chesterfield during the 1991/92 season?

438. How many of their 42 League matches did Chesterfield win in Division 3 during the 1994/95 season – 23, 26 or 29?

439. Which Chesterfield player scored a last-minute equaliser in a 1-1 away League draw against Carlisle United in April 1995?

440. In what position in Division 2 did Chesterfield finish in the 1995/96 season?

SQUAD NUMBERS 2009/2010

Match up the player with his squad number for the season

441.	Darren Currie	18
442.	Derek Niven	21
443.	Jack Lester	17
444.	Robert Page	1
445.	Kevin Austin	8
446.	Dan Gray	5
447.	Daniel Hall	6
448.	Lewis Montrose	14
449.	Lloyd Kerry	10
450.	Tommy Lee	7

MARK ALLOTT

451. Against which team did Mark make his Chesterfield League debut, in a 2-2 away draw in December 2001?

452. From which team did Mark sign when he joined Chesterfield, initially on loan in 2001 and then permanently in 2002?

453. In which year was Mark born – 1976, 1977 or 1978?

454. What is Mark's middle name – Stephen, Sean or Scott?

455. True or false: Mark scored for Chesterfield in both his second and third League appearances during the 2001/02 season?

456. Which team did Mark join when he left Chesterfield in July 2007?

457. Against which team did Mark score a brace for Chesterfield in a 3-2 away League win in September 2005?

458. True or false: Mark was voted Chesterfield's club's player of the year and supporters' player of the year in 2005/06?

459. In what position did Mark play while at Chesterfield?

460. From which club did Mark sign when he re-joined Chesterfield during July 2009, having been at the club for only 8 weeks and never playing a competitive game for them?

DANNY WILSON

461. How many League games did Danny play for Chesterfield in his career – 100, 150 or 200?

462. From which club did Danny sign when he joined Chesterfield?

463. Following on from the previous question, in what year did Danny join Chesterfield?

464. True or false: Danny managed Chesterfield during the 1998/99 season?

465. For which country did Danny win 24 full international caps, scoring 1 goal?

466. In which year was Danny born – 1960, 1965 or 1970?

467. In what position did Danny play during his playing days?

468. Which Spireites manager signed Danny for Chesterfield?

469. Which team did Danny join when he left The Spireites in 1983?

470. How many League goals did Danny score in his Chesterfield career – 9, 11 or 13?

ANDY MORRIS

471. What was Andy's nickname while at Chesterfield?

472. In what year did Andy join Chesterfield?

473. From which club did Andy sign when he joined Chesterfield?

474. Against which team did Andy score a Chesterfield hat-trick during the 1988/89 season?

475. Against which club did Chesterfield play in Andy's testimonial in 1998?

476. How many League goals did Andy score for Chesterfield – 55, 65 or 75?

477. What is Andy's middle name – Dean, Daniel or Damien?

478. Which team did Andy join when he left Chesterfield in 1998?

479. In what position did Andy play during his playing days?

480. How many League appearances did Andy make in his Chesterfield career – 244, 266 or 288?

LEGENDS – 2

*Rearrange the letters to reveal the name
of a Chesterfield legend*

481. HITKE TOSTS

482. HONJ YILRED

483. KAFNR HATRECK

484. VESTE YAPEN

485. CAKJ YODMO

486. NAST RUNLIMB

487. EINER SOMS

488. OSERMEN LAMPERS

489. AJKC ELE

490. KARM LEJUS

LEE ROGERS

491. What was Lee's nickname at Chesterfield?

492. How many League goals did Lee score as a Chesterfield player – 1, 2 or 3?

493. Against which club did Lee score his first Chesterfield goal?

494. In what position did Lee play during his playing days?

495. What job did Lee take up when he retired from professional football?

496. Against which team did Lee play in his testimonial in 1996?

497. From which club did Lee join Chesterfield in 1986?

498. Lee made his final League appearance for the club and left Chesterfield in what year?

499. Which Chesterfield manager handed Lee his first team debut?

500. How many League appearances did Lee make during his Chesterfield career – 224, 334 or 444?

LEAGUE GOALSCORERS – 2

Match up the player with the number of League goals he scored for Chesterfield

501.	Jackie Fisher	44
502.	Brian Frear	25
503.	Steve Norris	56
504.	Jimmy Cookson	31
505.	Ray McHale	96
506.	Andy Morris	58
507.	Jon Howard	85
508.	Keith Havenhand	27
509.	Kevin Randall	86
510.	Phil Bonnyman	39

WHERE DID THEY COME FROM? – 2

Match up the player with the club he left to join Chesterfield

511.	Frank Barlow	*Luton Town*
512.	Danny Hall	*Leicester City*
513.	Tommy Lee	*Manchester United*
514.	Darren Currie	*Bury*
515.	Joe Ball	*Rochdale*
516.	Allan Sliman	*Gretna*
517.	Walter McMillen	*Burnley*
518.	Norman Kirkman	*Sheffield United*
519.	Walter Harrison	*Macclesfield Town*
520.	Arthur Bellamy	*Bristol City*

1970s

521. Which Chesterfield player scored twice on his club debut, in a 5-1 home win in the League Cup in August 1979?

522. In what position did Chesterfield finish in Division 3 during the 1973/74 season?

523. How many Chesterfield League hat-tricks were scored during the 1970s?

524. How much was a Chesterfield match-day programme during the 1978/79 season?

525. Who were Chesterfield playing at home when they recorded an attendance of 16,760 in a Division 3 match in August 1970?

526. Who took over as Chesterfield boss in October 1976?

527. Which Chesterfield goalkeeper and striker were ever present during the 1970/71 season?

528. In what position did Chesterfield finish in Division 3 during the 1977/78 season?

529. Which Chesterfield player scored for the club in a 3-2 League win when he came on as a substitute at Colchester United in February 1976?

530. How many of their 46 League games did Chesterfield win during the 1973/74 season – 20, 21 or 22?

ALAN STEVENSON

531. Which Chesterfield goalkeeper failed a fitness test, allowing Alan to make his full club debut?

532. In what year did Alan make his Spireites debut?

533. On average, how many goals did Alan concede during his Chesterfield career – 0.846, 1.846 or 2.846?

534. True or false: Alan once played cricket for Derbyshire's second team?

535. How many clean sheets did Alan keep during his time at Chesterfield in League competition – 14, 41, or 44?

536. In what year did Alan leave The Spireites?

537. True or false: Chesterfield lost 2-1 away on Alan's League debut against Scunthorpe United in Division 4?

538. How many League appearances did Alan make in his Chesterfield career – 84, 94 or 104?

539. Which team did Alan join when he left The Spireites?

540. True or false: Alan was an unused substitute for England in Lisbon in 1974?

PHIL PICKEN

541. In what year was Phil born – 1984, 1985 or 1986?

542. From which club did Phil sign on loan when he joined Chesterfield in 2005?

543. What is Phil's middle name – Justin, Jeremy or James?

544. Chesterfield loaned Phil to which club in January 2009?

545. Against which team did Phil score his first Chesterfield goal, in a 3-1 home defeat in April 2006?

546. Which Chesterfield manager signed Phil for the club?

547. How many yellow cards did Phil pick up while playing for Chesterfield during the 2006/07 season?

548. Against which team did Phil score Chesterfield's opening goal in a 3-0 home League win in February 2007?

549. What nationality is Phil – English, Welsh or Scottish?

550. Against which team did Phil make his Chesterfield debut, in a 4-1 away League defeat in August 2005?

WHERE DID THEY GO? – 2

*Match up the player with the club he joined
on leaving Chesterfield*

551.	Alan O'Hare	Hereford United
552.	Jamie Ward	Doncaster Rovers
553.	Paul Shaw	Notts County
554.	Gareth Davies	Northampton Town
555.	Peter Leven	Mansfield Town
556.	Daniel Williams	Oxford United
557.	Nathan Abbey	MK Dons
558.	Phil Robinson	Sheffield United
559.	Nicky Law	Halifax Town
560.	Lee Turnbull	Hereford United

1980s

561.   How much did a match-day programme cost at Chesterfield during the 1983/84 season?

562.   In what season during the 1980s did Chesterfield win Division 4?

563.   Following on from the previous question, how many of their 46 League matches did the club win – 26, 28 or 30?

564.   Which Chesterfield player scored a brace on his League debut against Oxford United in a 3-0 away win in September 1980?

565.   Which Chesterfield player scored a League hat-trick in a 4-0 home win against Cardiff City during the 1988/89 season?

566.   Who took over as Chesterfield boss during November 1988?

567.   Which two centre backs played in every League match during the 1984/85 season?

568.   Which Chesterfield player scored when he came on as a substitute in a 4-1 home League win against Fulham in December 1988?

569.   Which player made his League debut for Chesterfield during the 1987/88 season, making a total 119 League appearances and scoring 53 League goals for the club?

570.   In what position did Chesterfield finish in the League during the 1980/81 season in Division 3?

KEVIN DAVIES

571. In which year was Kevin born – 1977, 1978 or 1979?

572. Which team paid £7.5 million for Kevin in June 1998?

573. Against which team did Kevin score a Chesterfield hat-trick in a 3-2 away win in the FA Cup in February 1997?

574. Against which team did Kevin score Chesterfield's first goal in a 2-0 home win in the FA Cup 2nd round in December 1996?

575. For which club did Kevin play between 1999 and 2003?

576. How many League appearances did Kevin make for Chesterfield in his career – 128, 148 or 168?

577. In what year did Kevin make his Chesterfield League debut?

578. How many League goals did Kevin score for Chesterfield in his career – 20, 21 or 22?

579. How many League goals did Kevin score for Chesterfield during the 1996/97 season?

580. Which team did Kevin join when he left Chesterfield in May 1997?

AARON DOWNES

581. What nationality is Aaron?

582. In which year was Aaron born – 1985, 1987 or 1989?

583. What squad number did Aaron wear during the 2008/09 and 2009/10 seasons?

584. In what position does Aaron play?

585. Against which team did Aaron score for Chesterfield on his League debut for the club?

586. How many League goals did Aaron score for Chesterfield in his 42 League appearances during the 2008/09 season?

587. From which non-League club did Aaron sign when he joined Chesterfield?

588. What is Aaron's middle name – Terry, Tony or Timothy?

589. Which Chesterfield manager signed Aaron for the club in 2004?

590. In 2007 Aaron was made Chesterfield captain after which player left the club?

DEREK NIVEN

591. Against which team did Derek make his Chesterfield League debut, in a 2-2 home draw in December 2003?

592. Which Chesterfield manager signed Derek and handed him his club debut?

593. From which club did Derek sign when he joined Chesterfield?

594. In which year was Derek born in Falkirk – 1983, 1984 or 1985?

595. Against which team did Derek score a fantastic goal in the League Cup during the 2006/07 season?

596. In what position does Derek play?

597. How many League goals did Derek score for Chesterfield during the 2008/09 season?

598. Against which team did Derek score Chesterfield's winning goal in a 3-2 away League win in August 2007?

599. How many yellow cards did Derek pick up during the 2006/07 season in all competitions?

600. Against which team did Derek score his first Chesterfield goal, in a 1-0 home League win in April 2004?

CHESTERFIELD V. DONCASTER ROVERS

601. Which midfielder scored Chesterfield's only goal in a 1-0 away League win over Doncaster in February 2005?

602. Who scored Chesterfield's equaliser in a 1-1 home League draw in March 2007?

603. What was the score when the sides first met in the League in September 1901?

604. In which division were the teams playing during the 1991/92 season?

605. True or false: Chesterfield beat Doncaster both home and away during the 1994/95 League season?

606. Which striker scored a 63rd-minute equaliser for Chesterfield in a 1-1 draw at Belle Vue in January 2006?

607. What was the score when the sides met at the Recreation Ground in the League in October 2004?

608. True or false: the clubs didn't meet in the League during the 1970s?

609. What was the score when the teams met at the Recreation Ground in the League on Boxing Day 1986?

610. Which team won the FA Cup replay after drawing 3-3 four days earlier in November 1960?

CHESTERFIELD V. NOTTS COUNTY

611. Which Chesterfield forward scored the only goal in a 1-0 away League win in January 2009?

612. What was the score when Chesterfield played Notts County at home in the League in October 2008?

613. True or false: during their history the clubs met in the FA Cup before they met in the League?

614. What was the score when Chesterfield played Notts County at home in October 1969?

615. In which season during the 1960s did the sides meet in the League Cup?

616. Which Chesterfield player scored an 84th-minute winner in a 2-1 home victory in the League in December 2001?

617. Which forward scored a Chesterfield brace in a 2-1 home League win in April 2000?

618. What is Notts County's nickname?

619. Which midfielder scored a Chesterfield brace in a 3-0 home League win in October 1998?

620. What is the name of the stadium that Chesterfield visit when they play Notts County away from home?

2005/2006

621. Who was Chesterfield's manager during this season?

622. How many of their 46 League matches did Chesterfield win – 12, 14 or 16?

623. Which team did Chesterfield beat 4-3 at home in the League in October 2005?

624. With which team did Chesterfield share a 2-2 away draw on Boxing Day 2005, with Paul Hall and Shane Nicholson scoring for The Spireites?

625. Which team did Chesterfield beat 3-1 away on the opening day of the League season?

626. Which three goalkeepers played in the 46 League games this season?

627. Which midfielder finished as the club's highest scorer with 15 League goals?

628. How many players made their Chesterfield League debut this season?

629. Which player left Chesterfield for Notts County in January 2006?

630. In which position did Chesterfield finish in the League – 12th, 14th or 16th?

DAVID REEVES

631. In which year was David born in Birkenhead – 1965, 1966 or 1967?

632. From which team did David join Chesterfield in November 1997?

633. How many League goals did David score for Chesterfield during the 2000/01 season – 10, 13 or 16?

634. Against which team did David score a Chesterfield hat-trick (including two penalties) during a 4-4 home League draw in March 2004?

635. For which team did David play from1989 to 1993?

636. How many League appearances did David make for Chesterfield in his football career – 139, 239 or 339?

637. Which club did David join when he left Chesterfield in January 2002?

638. Against which club did David score his first Chesterfield goal, in a 1-0 win on his League debut in November 1997?

639. How many League goals did David score for Chesterfield during the 1998/99 season – 10, 13 or 16?

640. How many of Chesterfield's goals did David score in their 4-2 home League win against Cambridge United in August 1999?

WHO SCORED?

641. Who scored a hat-trick in a 3-1 home League win against Tranmere Rovers during the 1966/67 season?

642. Who scored 4 League hat-tricks for Chesterfield during the 1930/31 season?

643. Who scored 39 League goals in 70 appearances during his Chesterfield career in the early 1930s?

644. Who scored for Chesterfield after coming on as a substitute against Grimsby Town in a 2-1 home League win in March 2009?

645. Who scored 5 League hat-tricks for Chesterfield during the 1925/26 season?

646. Who scored a hat-trick in a 6-0 home League win against West Ham United during the 1947/48 season?

647. Who scored 20 League goals in 91 appearances for Chesterfield during the 2005/06 and 2006/07 seasons?

648. Who scored Chesterfield's first League goal of the 2008/09 season, in a 3-1 away win against Barnet in August 2008?

649. True or false: Jimmy Cookson scored 4 League hat-tricks for Chesterfield during the 1926/27 season?

650. Who scored a hat-trick in a 6-1 home League win against Accrington Stanley during the 1954/55 season?

2003/2004

651.   Who managed Chesterfield during this season?

652.   In what position did Chesterfield finish in the League?

653.   Which striker scored 13 League goals, finishing as the club's highest scorer this season?

654.   True or false: Chesterfield drew in their first four League matches of the season?

655.   Which team did Chesterfield beat 1-0 on the last day of the season?

656.   Following on from the previous question, can you name the striker who scored the only goal in the game?

657.   Which team beat Chesterfield 7-0 away in the League in January 2004?

658.   Which team did Chesterfield beat 2-1 at home on Boxing Day 2003?

659.   What was the score when Chesterfield visited Oakwell to play Barnsley in December 2003?

660.   Which London club did Chesterfield beat 4-2 at home in January 2004?

CHESTERFIELD V. DERBY COUNTY

661. True or false: when the teams met for the first time in their history, it was in an FA Cup tie in 1907?

662. In which competition did the sides meet during the 1968/69 season?

663. Following on from the previous question, which team won the game 3-0?

664. In what season during the 1980s did the teams meet for the last time in League competition, playing in Division 3?

665. What was the score when the teams met in a League match in Division 3 North in April 1957 – 7-1 to Chesterfield, 7-1 to Derby County or a 7-7 draw?

666. True or false: the clubs have met in Division 1 during their history?

667. What was the score when the teams met at the Recreation Ground in February 1986?

668. How many of the two clubs' 10 League matches have Chesterfield won – 2, 4 or 6?

669. True or false: Chesterfield have never beaten Derby County in the League Cup or FA Cup?

670. True or false: the teams met in the League during the 1970s?

JIMMY McGUIGAN

671. In which year was Jimmy born in Addiewell, near Glasgow – 1914, 1924 or 1934?

672. Which club signed Jimmy in 1949 for £2,000 – Stockport County, Sunderland or Sheffield United?

673. Jimmy took over from which manager at Chesterfield?

674. In what year was Jimmy appointed Chesterfield manager – 1967, 1969 or 1971?

675. To which position in Division 4 did Jimmy guide Chesterfield in his first season in charge – 5th, 6th or 7th?

676. True or false: Jimmy was manager of Chesterfield when the club won the Division 4 title during 1969/70?

677. How many League matches did Jimmy manage Chesterfield – 276, 296 or 316?

678. How many League matches did Jimmy win as Chesterfield boss – 103, 113 or 123?

679. In what year did Jimmy leave Chesterfield as club manager?

680. Who succeeded Jimmy as Chesterfield manager when he left?

CHESTERFIELD V. ROTHERHAM UNITED

681. In which year did the clubs first meet in the League – 1913, 1923 or 1933?

682. True or false: Chesterfield beat Rotherham both at home and away in the first two meetings of their history?

683. Which defender scored the only goal of the match when Chesterfield beat Rotherham 1-0 away in the League in February 1996?

684. What was the score when the teams met at Millmoor in the League in February 2006?

685. Following on from the previous question, can you name the Chesterfield scorers in the game?

686. True or false: the clubs didn't meet in any competition during the 1940s, 1950s and 1960s?

687. Which team won the League Cup 1st round tie in August 2004 at Millmoor?

688. What was the aggregate score when the sides met in the League Cup 1st round, 1st and 2nd legs, in August 1998?

689. True or false: the teams have never met in the FA Cup?

690. Which defender scored the only goal of the match when Chesterfield beat Rotherham 1-0 in the League in September 2008?

2001/2002

691. Which goalkeeper played in all 46 League matches during this season?

692. How many of their 23 home League matches did Chesterfield win – 7, 8 or 9?

693. Can you name the three Oldham Athletic players that Chesterfield signed this season?

694. Which team did Luke Beckett join in December 2001 when he left the Recreation Ground?

695. Which forward scored an 88th-minute winner for Chesterfield against Blackpool in a 2-1 home League win in April 2002?

696. Which team beat Chesterfield 6-3 at the Recreation Ground on the opening day of the League season?

697. Which forward finished as the club's highest League scorer with nine goals?

698. Which manager took over from Nicky Law halfway through the season?

699. In which position did Chesterfield finish in the League – 18th, 19th or 20th?

700. Who scored a brace for Chesterfield in a 4-0 home League win against Oldham Athletic in January 2002?

LEAGUE POSITIONS - 2

*Match up the season with the club's
finishing position in the League*

701.	1980/81	1st in Division 4
702.	1981/82	18th in Division 3
703.	1982/83	13th in Division 4
704.	1983/84	22nd in Division 3
705.	1984/85	7th in Division 4
706.	1985/86	17th in Division 3
707.	1986/87	5th in Division 3
708.	1987/88	11th in Division 3
709.	1988/89	17th in Division 3
710.	1989/90	24th in Division 3

IAN BRECHIN

711. Against which team did Ian make his Chesterfield debut, in a 2-1 away League win in August 1997?

712. True or false: Ian won a full international cap for England during 2007?

713. Against which team did Ian score Chesterfield's second goal in a 2-0 home League win in February 2000?

714. In what year did Ian join Chesterfield for his second spell?

715. For which team did Ian play between 2005 and 2009?

716. Against which team did Ian score his first Chesterfield League goal, in an FA Cup 2nd round match in December 1997?

717. How many League goals did Ian score for Chesterfield during the 2000/01 season?

718. For which team did Ian sign when he left Chesterfield in June 2002?

719. In which year was Ian born in Rotherham – 1973, 1974 or 1975?

720. In what position does Ian play?

CHESTERFIELD V. SHEFFIELD UNITED

721. In which competition did the sides meet during the 2007/08 season?

722. Following on the previous question, what was the score in the game?

723. True or false: the sides met in the League and the FA Cup during the 1960s?

724. In which year did the sides first meet in the League, in a Division 2 match – 1934, 1936 or 1938?

725. Following on the previous question, what was the score in the game?

726. Apart from the two Division 3 matches during the 1980/81 season, in which other competition did the sides meet this season?

727. True or false: Chesterfield beat Sheffield United in both the home and away League matches during the 1988/89 season?

728. In what season did the teams first meet in the League Cup?

729. Which ground do Chesterfield visit when they play away against Sheffield United?

730. True or false: the sides did not meet in any competition during the 1990s?

JAMIE HEWITT

731. Against which team did Jamie make his League debut for Chesterfield, in a 0-0 away draw in November 1985?

732. Which Chesterfield manager handed Jamie his League debut?

733. How many League goals did Jamie score in his Chesterfield career – 16, 26 or 36?

734. Against which team did Jamie score his only Chesterfield League goal during the 1997/98 season?

735. In what position did Jamie play during his playing days?

736. Against which London club did Jamie score the only goal in a 1-0 League win in April 1999?

737. When Jamie left The Spireites in August 1992 he joined which club, later returning to Chesterfield for a second spell in October 1993?

738. In which year was Jamie born in Chesterfield – 1966, 1967 or 1968?

739. How many League appearances did Jamie make during his Chesterfield career – 406, 506 or 606?

740. Who is the only player in the club's history to have played more League matches than Jamie?

WAYNE ALLISON

741.   What is Wayne's middle name – Anthony, Alan or Arnold?

742.   What is Wayne's nickname?

743.   From which team did Wayne join Chesterfield in 2004?

744.   Which Spireites manager signed Wayne for the club?

745.   Against which team did Wayne make his Chesterfield League debut, in a 3-1 home win in August 2004?

746.   True or false: Wayne scored on his Chesterfield League debut?

747.   How many League goals did Wayne score for The Spireites in his first season at the club?

748.   Against which London team did Wayne score a brace for Chesterfield in a 5-1 home win in August 2006?

749.   How many League goals did Wayne score in his Chesterfield career – 22, 33 or 44?

750.   Against which team did Wayne score the last competitive goal of his career, in a 3-1 home defeat in the Football League Trophy in September 2007?

CHESTERFIELD V. GRIMSBY TOWN

751. What was the score in the two clubs' first ever League meeting in December 1899?

752. Which Scottish midfielder scored Chesterfield's winning goal in a 2-1 home League win in March 2009?

753. What was the score when the sides met at the Recreation Ground in the League in March 2004?

754. Following on from the previous question, who scored a hat-trick for Chesterfield?

755. In which season during the 1990s did the teams meet in the FA Cup?

756. In which division were the clubs playing when they met in the League during the 1989/90 season?

757. In which season during the 1960s did the sides met in the League Cup for the first time in their history?

758. Which Chesterfield midfielder scored the only goal in a 1-0 away win in August 2008?

759. Who scored Chesterfield's only goal in a 1-0 away win in a League Cup tie in September 2002?

760. True or false: Grimsby Town beat Chesterfield both home and away in the League during the 1969/70 season?

CALEB FOLAN

761. What is Caleb's middle name – Colman, Carter or Cambell?

762. How many League goals did Caleb score for Chesterfield in his career?

763. Which team did Caleb join in January 2007 when he left Chesterfield?

764. Against which team did Caleb score a brace in a 3-2 away League win in August 2004?

765. Against which team did Caleb score a brace in a 3-1 home League win in September 2006?

766. In which year was Caleb born – 1980, 1981 or 1982?

767. Against which team did Caleb score his first Chesterfield goal, in a 1-1 League away draw in March 2003?

768. From which Yorkshire team did Caleb sign when he joined Chesterfield in 2003?

769. For which country did Caleb win his first international cap in 2008?

770. In what position does Caleb play?

2000/2001

771. Which team did Chesterfield beat 4-1 at the Recreation Ground on the opening day of the League season?

772. Which goalkeeper played in all 46 League matches this season?

773. Which striker, while on loan at Chesterfield, scored the club's winning goal in a 2-1 League home win against Blackpool in February 2001?

774. Who finished as the club's highest League scorer with 16 goals?

775. Which team did Chesterfield beat 2-0 on Boxing Day 2000 at the Recreation Ground?

776. How many of their 46 League matches did Chesterfield win – 25, 27 or 29?

777. True or false: Chesterfield won their first three League matches of the season?

778. Who managed Chesterfield during this season?

779. In which position in the League did Chesterfield finish – 3rd, 5th or 7th?

780. Which team did Chesterfield beat 3-0 at home on the last day of the League season?

AGAINST WHICH CLUB?

781. Which club would Chesterfield be playing if they visited Ashton Gate?

782. Which club would Chesterfield have played if they had visited the Athletic Ground or Recreation Ground, prior to the ground moving to Vale Park?

783. Which club would Chesterfield be playing if they visited Carrow Road?

784. Which club would Chesterfield have played if they had visited Linthorpe Road or Ayresome Park, before the ground moved to the Riverside Stadium?

785. Which club would Chesterfield be playing if they visited Meadow Lane?

786. Which club would Chesterfield have been playing if they had visited The McCain Stadium?

787. Which club would Chesterfield have played if they had visited The Den, before the ground moved to The New Den?

788. Which club would Chesterfield be playing if they visited London Road?

789. Which club would Chesterfield have played if they had visited Anlaby Road or Boothferry Park, before the ground moved to The Kingston Communication Stadium?

790. Which club would Chesterfield be playing if they visited The Hawthorns?

LEAGUE POSITIONS – 3

Match up the season with the club's finishing position in the league

791.	1990/91	7th in Division 2
792.	1991/92	9th in Division 2
793.	1992/93	10th in Division 2
794.	1993/94	10th in Division 2
795.	1994/95	13th in Division 4
796.	1995/96	24th in Division 2
797.	1996/97	18th in Division 4
798.	1997/98	8th in Division 3
799.	1998/99	12th in Division 3
800.	1999/2000	3rd in Division 3

ANSWERS

CLUB HISTORY

1. The Recreation Ground
2. 1969/70 and 1984/85
3. The Spireites
4. Ernie Moss
5. Jason Lee
6. Tottenham Hotspur
7. False
8. Anglo-Scottish Cup
9. Dave Blakey
10. 1996/97

MANAGERS - 1

11.	Harry Parkes	1922
12.	Arthur Cox	1976
13.	Jimmy McGuigan	1967
14.	Dave Rushbury	2002
15.	Teddy Davison	1952
16.	Frank Barlow	1980
17.	Nicky Law	2000
18.	Joe Shaw	1973
19.	Tom Callaghan	1919
20.	Lee Richardson	2007

JACK LESTER

21. William
22. Nottingham Forest
23. 14
24. Grimsby Town
25. Sheffield United
26. Lincoln City
27. True
28. Barnet
29. Lee Richardson
30. 1975

2008/2009

31. 10th

32.   *Lee Richardson*

33.   *Martin Gritton*

34.   *Exeter City*

35.   *Jamie Ward*

36.   *16: 8 at home and 0 away*

37.   *Jack Lester*

38.   *Chester City*

39.   *Jamie Ward and Scott Boden*

40.   *Jack Lester*

TOP LEAGUE APPEARANCES

41.	*Gerry Sears*	*412*
42.	*Ron Powell*	*471*
43.	*Shaun O'Neill*	*437 (5)*
44.	*Albert Phelan*	*385 (5)*
45.	*Horace Wass*	*413*
46.	*Ernie Moss*	*466 (3)*
47.	*Jamie Hewitt*	*488 (18)*
48.	*Andy Kowalski*	*373 (20)*
49.	*David Blakey*	*617*
50.	*Albert Holmes*	*467 (3)*

GORDON BANKS

51.   *1937*

52.   *Leicester City*

53.   *23*

54.   *Goalkeeper*

55.   *Stoke City*

56.   *73*

57.   *Teddy Davison*

58.   *Colchester United*

59.   *Third Division North*

60.   *False*

JIM BROWN

61.   *True: against Stockport County during October 1983*

62.   *182*

63.   *1*

64.   Goalkeeper
65.   Cardiff City
66.   He was appointed the clubs Commercial manager
67.   Albion Rovers
68.   True
69.   Jimmy McGuigan
70.   51

LEAGUE GOALSCORERS - 1

#	Name	Goals
71.	Ernie Moss	162
72.	Dave Waller	53
73.	Tony Lormor	34
74.	Jamie Hewitt	26
75.	Bob Newton	29
76.	Ivan Hollett	62
77.	Phil Walker	47
78.	Alan Birch	40
79.	Glynn Hurst	28
80.	Lee Turnbull	26

WHERE DID THEY COME FROM? – 1

#	Name	From
81.	David Reeves	Preston North End
82.	Ricky Green	Scunthorpe United
83.	Phil Bonnyman	Carlisle United
84.	Paul Holland	Sheffield United
85.	Geoff Salmons	Leicester City
86.	Steve Wilkinson	Preston North End
87.	Bill Green	Peterborough United
88.	John Turner	Torquay United
89.	Alan Birch	Walsall
90.	Jason Lee	Watford

MANAGERS - 2

#	Name	Year
91.	Roy McFarland	2003
92.	John Duncan (1st spell)	1983
93.	Bill Harvey	1932
94.	Paul Hart	1988
95.	Bob Brocklebank	1945

96.	Chris McMenemy	1991
97.	Tony McShane	1962
98.	Bob Marshall	1949
99.	John Duncan (2nd spell)	1993
100.	Frank Barlow	1980

CHESTERFIELD V. MANSFIELD TOWN

101. 3-1 to Chesterfield
102. Jamie Winter
103. True
104. Ryan Williams
105. The League Cup
106. Nicky Law
107. 1933
108. 3
109. David Moss
110. True: Chesterfield won 2-0 at home and 3-1 away

DEBUTS

111. David Dowson
112. Danny Gray
113. 11: Wayne Allison, Alan Bailey, Jamal Campbell-Ryce, Aaron Downes, Mark Stallard, Sammy Clingan, Jordan Fowler, Marton Fulop, Calos Logan, Glyn Thompson and Michael Fox
114. Kevin Cooper
115. 3: Kenny Burton, Eric Winstanley and Dave Thompson
116. True
117. David Bailey
118. True: Mike Pollitt, Luke Beckett, Lee Richardson, Sean Parrish, Steve Tutill and Jamie Ingledow
119. Arthur Albiston
120. Lee Askham

RON POWELL

121. 471
122. Manchester City
123. 1952
124. He ran a newsagents and grocery store

125.	Goalkeeper
126.	113
127.	1965
128.	False: he never scored a League goal for Chesterfield
129.	Mansfield Town (on 23 August 1952)
130.	734

NATIONALITIES

131.	Gregor Robertson	Scottish
132.	Kevin Austin	Trinidad & Tobago
133.	Robert Page	Welsh
134.	Alan Goodall	English
135.	Caleb Folan	Irish
136.	Jamie Lowry	English
137.	Derek Niven	Scottish
138.	Lewis Montrose	English
139.	Martin Gritton	Scottish
140.	Aaron Downes	Australian

1960s

141.	12th
142.	Terry Foley
143.	John Roberts
144.	Dave Blakey
145.	16th
146.	Tony McShane
147.	Workington
148.	7th
149.	Billy Stark (against Tranmere Rovers) and Ivan Hollett (against Wrexham)
150.	10: Tony Bartley, Kevin Randall, Bobby Tait, Andy Wilson, Billy Stark, Des Anderson, Peter Neale, Alan Stopford, Malcolm Brunt and Stuart Parsons

JOHN SHERIDAN

151.	2009
152.	Oldham Athletic
153.	Midfielder

154. Joseph
155. 5
156. False
157. 1964
158. Tommy Wright
159. Manchester United
160. Leeds United

ALBERT HOLMES

161. 1960
162. Defender
163. Cambridge United
164. 1974
165. Jim McGuigan
166. Paul Holmes
167. 470: 467 (3)
168. False: he never won a full international cap for England
169. 10
170. He became a gas engineer

GOALSCORING DEBUTANTS

171.	Martin Gritton	Chester City (January 2009), 3-1 away win
172.	Phil Cliff	Rochdale (February 1971), 1-1 home draw
173.	Bill Curry	Barnsley (January 1968), 3-2 home defeat
174.	Mark Innes	Brighton & Hove Albion (December 2001), 2-2 away draw
175.	Walter Ponting	Southampton (August 1936), 3-2 away defeat
176.	Frank Large	Rochdale (November 1972), 2-1 away win
177.	Mark Jules	Gillingham (August 1993), 2-0 away win
178.	Sean Parrish	York City (August 2000), 4-1 home win

| 179. | Norman Whitfield | Barrow (August 1922), 2-1 home win |
| 180. | Colin Cook | Bury (October 1932), 3-1 home defeat |

ERNIE MOSS

181. 1949
182. Striker
183. 3
184. False: he never managed Chesterfield
185. Bradford (Park Avenue)
186. 162
187. Sheffield United
188. True: the only penalty he took was in his testimonial, which he missed
189. 468: 466 (2)
190. True: he holds the record with 162 League goals (then Herbert Munday with 197 goals and George Smith with 98 goals)

2006/2007

191. Bournemouth
192. Paul Hall and Wayne Allison
193. 21st
194. Mansfield Town
195. Derek Niven and Aaron Downes
196. Jamie Ward
197. Port Vale
198. Paul Shaw
199. Jamie Ward
200. 12

MANAGERS – LEAGUE WINS

201.	Lee Richardson	37 wins out of 101 games
202.	Dave Rushbury	19 wins out of 66 games
203.	Chris McMenemy	33 wins out of 93 games
204.	Harry Parkes	101 wins out of 202 games
205.	Alec Campbell	4 wins out of 15 games
206.	Arthur Cox	68 wins out of 180 games

207.	Duggie Livingstone	59 wins out of 182 games
208.	Bob Marshall	46 wins out of 142 games
209.	Paul Hart	34 wins out of 100 games
210.	Nicky Law	34 wins out of 76 games

THE FA CUP

211. Gainsborough Trinity
212. Ipswich Town
213. Middlesbrough
214. Sheffield Wednesday
215. True
216. 1-0
217. False: Chesterfield have never won this competition in their history (Tottenham Hotspur won the FA Cup in 1981)
218. Wolverhampton Wanderers
219. 5th round (knocked out by Tottenham Hotspur)
220. True

JOHN DUNCAN

221. False: he never played for Chesterfield
222. Centre forward
223. Pearson
224. Frank Barlow
225. 1949
226. 1994/95
227. The Division 4 Championship
228. Scunthorpe United
229. Dundee
230. Chris McMenemy

THE STADIUM

231. £340
232. S40 4SX
233. 30,986
234. Newcastle United
235. True
236. 113 x 71 yards
237. The Main Stand, The Spion Kop, The Compton Street Stand

and the Cross Street Terrace Stand

238.   8,504

239.   1884

240.   01246

LEGENDS – 1

241.   Jimmy Cookson

242.   Kevin Davies

243.   Jim Brown

244.   Marcus Ebdon

245.   Gary Bellamy

246.   Alan Birch

247.   Dave Waller

248.   Horace Wass

249.   Lee Rogers

250.   David Reeves

GOALKEEPERS' CLEAN SHEETS

251.   19

252.   Chris Marples

253.   11

254.   Jack Moody

255.   Steve Ogrizovic

256.   Phil Morgan

257.   224

258.   8

259.   Billy Mercer

260.   Ron Powell

2004/2005

261.   17th

262.   Tcham N'Toya

263.   Barnet

264.   Jack Lester

265.   Luton Town

266.   Calos Logan

267.   Jamie Ward

268.   True

| 269. | Chester City |
| 270. | 14 |

DAVE BLAKEY

271.	20
272.	1948
273.	West Bromwich Albion
274.	Centre back
275.	6
276.	1967
277.	True
278.	Record appearance holder
279.	For dissent
280.	617

WHO AM I?

281.	Bob Brocklebank
282.	Bryan Frear
283.	George Smith
284.	John Sheridan
285.	Keith Havenhand
286.	Martin Gritton
287.	Albert Pynegar
288.	Gregor Robertson
289.	Lee Turnbull
290.	Danny Hall

NICKY LAW

291.	1961
292.	Arsenal
293.	Rotherham United
294.	1996
295.	John Duncan
296.	Division 3 promotion, finishing runners-up in the League
297.	False: he was a defender
298.	11
299.	True: Chesterfield lost 4-1 away to Preston North End in Division 4 in October 1993

PLAYER POSITIONS

301.	Billy Kidd	Left back
302.	Cliff Carr	Left back
303.	Gerry Sears	Left back
304.	Ron Powell	Goalkeeper
305.	Mark Williams	Centre back
306.	Tom Curtis	Midfielder
307.	Stan Milburn	Right back
308.	Freddie Capel	Right back
309.	Arnold Birch	Goalkeeper
310.	Ernie Moss	Forward

2007/2008

311.   19: Jack Lester, Gregor Robertson, Jamie Winter, Peter Leven, Steve Fletcher, Kevin Gray, Adam Rooney, Ben Algar, Felix Bastiens, Nicky Travis, Michael Barnes, Brendan Moloney, Kevin Cooper, Lloyd Kerry, David Dowson, Peter Hartley, Colin Hawkins, Graeme Owens and Bruce Dyer

312.   Lee Richardson

313.   8th

314.   25

315.   Peterborough United

316.   Kevin Cooper and Jamie Ward

317.   False: no players played in every League game (Barry Roche played in 45 out of the 46 League matches)

318.   12

319.   Lincoln City

320.   19

HAT-TRICK HEROES

321.   Jamie Ward

322.   5

323.   7-0 to Chesterfield

324.   George Milburn

325.   9

326.   The FA Cup

327.   David Reeves

328.   False: one hat-trick was scored by Paul Hall (against Bristol City, in a 4-2 away win)

329.   Mansfield Town

330.   Sean Parrish

CHESTERFIELD V. NOTTINGHAM FOREST

331.   False: Nottingham Forest won 3-1

332.   FA Cup (5th round)

333.   Tom Curtis

334.   Aaron Downes

335.   Division 2

336.   7-1 to Chesterfield

337.   The League Cup

338.   True: Chesterfield won 2-1 at home and 1-0 away

339.   False: they didn't meet in any of these decades in any competition

340.   Phil Picken

ROY McFARLAND

341.   2003

342.   175 (88 at home and 87 away)

343.   50 (31 at home and 19 away)

344.   The win was his 15th game in charge (during October 2003). His first 14 games ended in 7 draws (1 in the League Cup, losing 3-2 on penalties against Burnley) and 7 defeats

345.   28

346.   Central defender

347.   Leslie

348.   Cambridge United

349.   2007

350.   Lee Richardson

2002/2003

351.   David Reeves

352.   13: Ian Evatt, Gus Uhlenbeek, Damon Searle, Mark DeBolla, Adam Smith, Marvin Robinson, Jamie Cade, Paul Warhurst, Derek Niven, Matt O'Halloran, Jamie McMaster, Tcham N'Toya

and Jamie Fullarton
353.	20th
354.	Mark Hudson
355.	Dave Rushbury
356.	Glynn Hurst
357.	Northampton Town
358.	4-0 to Chesterfield
359.	True
360.	14

LOAN PLAYERS

361.	Jamie O'Hara	Tottenham Hotspur (2005/06)
362.	Ian Seddon	Chester City (1975/76)
363.	John Roberts	Blackburn Rovers (1967/68)
364.	Peter Hartley	Sunderland (2007/08)
365.	Jordan Fowler	Arsenal (2004/05)
366.	Carl Airey	Charleroi (1986/87)
367.	Charlie Daniels	Tottenham Hotspur (2006/07)
368.	David Hanson	Leyton Orient (1996/97)
369.	Graham Hyde	Birmingham City (2001/02)
370.	Steve Phillips	Peterborough United (1987/88)

MATCH THE YEAR

371.	Ambrose Brown scored five goals for Chesterfield against Mansfield Town	1935
372.	Chesterfield beat Scunthorpe United 5-0 in the League	1972
373.	The club were Division 3 North Champions	1931
374.	The club reached the FA Cup semi-finals	1997
375.	Chesterfield beat Mansfield Town 5-0 in the League	1971
376.	The club reached their highest Football League position: 4th in Division 2	1947
377.	The club recorded their record attendance of 30,561 v. Tottenham Hotspur in the FA Cup	1938
378.	The club were Division 3 play-off winners	1996
379.	The club were Division 4 Champions	1970
380.	Burnley beat Chesterfield 7-0 in the FA Cup	1957

LEAGUE POSITIONS – 1

381.	1960/61	24th in Division 3
382.	1961/62	19th in Division 4
383.	1962/63	15th in Division 4
384.	1963/64	16th in Division 4
385.	1964/65	12th in Division 4
386.	1965/66	20th in Division 4
387.	1966/67	15th in Division 4
388.	1967/68	7th in Division 4
389.	1968/69	20th in Division 4
390.	1969/70	1st in Division 4

THE LEAGUE CUP

391. Leyton Orient

392. Charlton Athletic

393. 1964/65

394. Scunthorpe United

395. Liverpool

396. Mansfield Town

397. Aston Villa

398. Bryan Frear (against Leyton Orient in the 2nd round in November 1960)

399. West Ham United

400. False: the club have never won this competition

TRANSFERS

401.	Joe Ball	Chesterfield paid Bury £400
402.	Harry Roberts	Birmingham City paid Chesterfield £10,600
403.	Willis Edwards	Leeds United paid Chesterfield £1,500
404.	Allan Sliman	Chesterfield paid Bristol City £1,500
405.	Bill Green	Chesterfield paid Peterborough United £40,000
406.	Paul Holland	Chesterfield paid Sheffield United £150,000
407.	Joe Cooper	Notts County paid Chesterfield £1,000

408.	Ellis Gee	Everton paid Chesterfield £100
409.	Jimmy Cookson	West Bromwich Albion paid Chesterfield £2,500
410.	Geoff Salmons	Chesterfield paid Leicester City £35,000

CHESTERFIELD V. SHEFFIELD WEDNESDAY

411. True

412. Sammy Clingan

413. 3-1 to Chesterfield

414. Glynn Hurst

415. False: the teams have never met in the League Cup

416. Sheffield Wednesday (5-1)

417. 1975/76 (1-0 at home and 3-1 away)

418. 0-0

419. Mark DeBolla

420. 1946/47 (4-2 at home and 1-0 away)

WHERE DID THEY GO? – 1

421.	Kevin Davies	Southampton
422.	Alan Birch	Wolves
423.	Jim Brown	Sheffield United
424.	Alan Stevenson	Burnley
425.	Gordon Dale	Portsmouth
426.	Harry Roberts	Birmingham City
427.	Billy Whitaker	Middlesbrough
428.	Harry Clifton	Newcastle United
429.	Albert Malam	Huddersfield Town
430.	Jimmy Cookson	West Bromwich Albion

1990s

431. Sean Dyche

432. Mark Jules

433. David Lancaster

434. Chris McMenemy

435. 1994/95

436. Andy Scott

437. £1

438. 23
439. David Moss
440. 7th

SQUAD NUMBERS 2009/2010

441.	Darren Currie	10
442.	Derek Niven	8
443.	Jack Lester	14
444.	Robert Page	5
445.	Kevin Austin	6
446.	Dan Gray	21
447.	Daniel Hall	18
448.	Lewis Montrose	7
449.	Lloyd Kerry	17
450.	Tommy Lee	1

MARK ALLOTT

451. Brighton & Hove Albion
452. Oldham Athletic
453. 1977
454. Stephen
455. True: both games at home, against Notts County and Oldham Athletic
456. Oldham Athletic
457. Walsall
458. True
459. Midfielder
460. Tranmere Rovers

DANNY WILSON

461. 100
462. Bury
463. 1980
464. False: he was never Chesterfield manager
465. Northern Ireland
466. 1960
467. Midfielder
468. Arthur Cox

469.   *Nottingham Forest*

470.   *13*

ANDY MORRIS

471.   *Bruno*

472.   *1988*

473.   *Rotherham United*

474.   *Cardiff City*

475.   *Nottingham Forest*

476.   *55*

477.   *Dean*

478.   *Rochdale*

479.   *Centre forward*

480.   *266: 225 (41)*

LEGENDS – 2

481.   *Keith Stott*

482.   *John Ridley*

483.   *Frank Thacker*

484.   *Steve Payne*

485.   *Jack Moody*

486.   *Stan Milburn*

487.   *Ernie Moss*

488.   *Emerson Marples*

489.   *Jack Lee*

490.   *Mark Jules*

LEE ROGERS

491.   *Nobby*

492.   *1*

493.   *Lincoln*

494.   *Defender*

495.   *Police officer*

496.   *Nottingham Forest*

497.   *Doncaster Rovers*

498.   *1998*

499.   *John Duncan*

500.   *334: 310 (24)*

LEAGUE GOALSCORERS - 2

501.	Jackie Fisher	31
502.	Brian Frear	86
503.	Steve Norris	44
504.	Jimmy Cookson	85
505.	Ray McHale	27
506.	Andy Morris	56
507.	Jon Howard	39
508.	Keith Havenhand	58
509.	Kevin Randall	96
510.	Phil Bonnyman	25

WHERE DID THEY COME FROM? – 2

511.	Frank Barlow	Sheffield United
512.	Danny Hall	Gretna
513.	Tommy Lee	Macclesfield Town
514.	Darren Currie	Luton Town
515.	Joe Ball	Bury
516.	Allan Sliman	Bristol City
517.	Walter McMillen	Manchester United
518.	Norman Kirkman	Rochdale
519.	Walter Harrison	Leicester City
520.	Arthur Bellamy	Burnley

1970s

521.	Alan Birch
522.	5th
523.	3: Ernie Moss (1970/71), Terry Shanahan (1975/76) and Rod Fern (1976/77)
524.	15p
525.	Aston Villa
526.	Arthur Cox
527.	Alan Stevenson and Kevin Randall
528.	9th
529.	Malcolm Darling
530.	21

ALAN STEVENSON

531.   Alan Humphreys

532.   1969 (October)

533.   0.846

534.   True

535.   41

536.   1972 (January)

537.   False: Chesterfield won 2-1

538.   104

539.   Burnley

540.   True

PHIL PICKEN

541.   1985

542.   Manchester United

543.   James

544.   Notts County

545.   Nottingham Forest

546.   Roy McFarland

547.   8

548.   Port Vale

549.   English

550.   Oldham Athletic

WHERE DID THEY GO? – 2

551.	Alan O'Hare	Mansfield Town
552.	Jamie Ward	Sheffield United
553.	Paul Shaw	Oxford United
554.	Gareth Davies	Halifax Town
555.	Peter Leven	MK Dons
556.	Daniel Williams	Hereford United
557.	Nathan Abbey	Northampton Town
558.	Phil Robinson	Notts County
559.	Nicky Law	Hereford United
560.	Lee Turnbull	Doncaster Rovers

1980s

561.   40p

562. 1984/85
563. 26
564. Keith Walwyn
565. Andy Morris
566. Paul Hart
567. Steve Baines and Les Hunter
568. Gavin McDonald
569. Dave Waller
570. 5th

KEVIN DAVIES

571. 1977
572. Blackburn Rovers
573. Bolton Wanderers
574. Scarborough
575. Southampton
576. 128: 113 (15)
577. 1993
578. 22
579. 3
580. Southampton

AARON DOWNES

581. Australian
582. 1985
583. 15
584. Centre back (defender)
585. MK Dons
586. 2
587. Frickley Athletic
588. Terry
589. Roy MacFarland
590. Mark Allott

DEREK NIVEN

591. Tranmere Rovers
592. Roy McFarland
593. Bolton Wanderers

594.   *1983*

595.   *Manchester City*

596.   *Midfielder*

597.   *2*

598.   *Peterborough United*

599.   *7 (6 in the League and 1 in the League Cup)*

600.   *Blackpool*

CHESTERFIELD V. DONCASTER ROVERS

601.   *Tcham N'Toya*

602.   *Paul Hall*

603.   *0-0*

604.   *Division 4*

605.   *True: 2-0 at home and 3-1 away*

606.   *Wayne Allison*

607.   *0-0*

608.   *False: they met during the 1970/71 season*

609.   *4-1 to Chesterfield*

610.   *Chesterfield: 1-0*

CHESTERFIELD V. NOTTS COUNTY

611.   *Drew Talbot*

612.   *3-1 to Chesterfield*

613.   *True: FA Cup 1930/31 and League 1931/32*

614.   *5-0 to Chesterfield*

615.   *1965/66*

616.   *Mark Allott*

617.   *David Reeves*

618.   *The Magpies*

619.   *Paul Holland*

620.   *Meadow Lane*

2005/2006

621.   *Roy McFarland*

622.   *14*

623.   *Huddersfield Town*

624.   *Scunthorpe United*

625.   *Blackpool*

626. *Barry Roche (41), Carl Muggleton (3) and Robert Beckwith (2)*

627. *Paul Hall*

628. *13: Barry Roche, Paul Hall, Reuben Hazell, Janos Kovacs, Colin Larkin, Phil Picken, Kevan Hurst, Sam Lancaster, Jamie O'Hara, Colin Heath, Rob Beckwith, Ashley Foyle and Jamie Jackson*

629. *Mark DeBolla*

630. *16th*

DAVID REEVES

631. *1967*

632. *Preston North End*

633. *13*

634. *Grimsby Town*

635. *Bolton Wanderers*

636. *239: 214 (25)*

637. *Oldham Athletic*

638. *Grimsby Town*

639. *10*

640. *4 (including 2 penalties)*

WHO SCORED?

641. *Billy Stark*

642. *Albert Pynegar*

643. *Samuel Abel*

644. *Derek Niven*

645. *Jimmy Cookson*

646. *Tommy Capel*

647. *Paul Hall*

648. *Jack Lester*

649. *True*

650. *Bill Sowden*

2003/2004

651. *Roy McFarland*

652. *20th*

653. *Glynn Hurst*

654. *True*

655. *Luton Town*

656. **Glynn Hurst**

657. **Plymouth Argyle**

658. **Peterborough United**

659. **1-0 to Chesterfield**

660. **Queens Park Rangers**

CHESTERFIELD V. DERBY COUNTY

661. *True*

662. **League Cup**

663. **Derby County**

664. **1985/86**

665. **7-1 to Derby County**

666. **False**

667. **1-0 to Chesterfield**

668. **2**

669. **True: FA Cup - 1 draw and 2 defeats; League Cup - 1 defeat**

670. **False: they didn't meet in any competition during this decade**

JIMMY McGUIGAN

671. **1924**

672. **Stockport County**

673. **Tony McShane**

674. **1967**

675. **7th**

676. **True**

677. **276 (138 at home and 138 away)**

678. **113 (77 at home and 36 away)**

679. **1973**

680. **Joe Shaw**

CHESTERFIELD V. ROTHERHAM UNITED

681. **1923**

682. **True (3-1 at home and 2-1 away)**

683. **Mark Jules**

684. **4-0 to Chesterfield**

685. **Kevan Hurst, Derek Niven, Mark Allott and Jamie O'Hara**

686. **True**

687. **Rotherham United (2-1)**

688.   3-0 (Chesterfield won 1-0 away and 2-0 at home)

689.   True

690.   Alan Goodall

2001/2002

691.   Nathan Abbey

692.   9

693.   Danny Walsh, Mark Innes and Mark Allott

694.   Stockport County

695.   Jamie Burt

696.   Colchester United

697.   Glynn Hurst

698.   Dave Rushbury

699.   18th

700.   Glynn Hurst

LEAGUE POSITIONS - 2

701.	1980/81	5th in Division 3
702.	1981/82	11th in Division 3
703.	1982/83	24th in Division 3
704.	1983/84	13th in Division 4
705.	1984/85	1st in Division 4
706.	1985/86	17th in Division 3
707.	1986/87	17th in Division 3
708.	1987/88	18th in Division 3
709.	1988/89	22nd in Division 3
710.	1989/90	7th in Division 4

IAN BRECHIN

711.   Wigan Athletic

712.   False: Ian hasn't won any international caps

713.   Reading

714.   2009

715.   Nottingham Forest

716.   Grimsby Town

717.   3

718.   Wigan Athletic

719.   1975

720.   Central defender

CHESTERFIELD V. SHEFFIELD UNITED
721.   League Cup (1st round)
722.   3-1 to Sheffield United
723.   False: they didn't meet in any competition during the 1960s
724.   1936
725.   2-2
726.   FA Cup (2nd round)
727.   True: 2-1 at home and 3-1 away
728.   1974/75
729.   Bramall Lane
730.   True

JAMIE HEWITT
731.   Plymouth Argyle
732.   John Duncan
733.   26
734.   Preston North End (in a 3-2 home win in August 1997)
735.   Midfielder
736.   Fulham
737.   Doncaster Rovers
738.   1968
739.   506: 488 (18)
740.   Dave Blakey (with 617 League appearances)

WAYNE ALLISON
741.   Anthony
742.   Chief
743.   Sheffield United
744.   Roy McFarland
745.   Brentford
746.   True: he scored one of Chesterfield's 3 goals
747.   6
748.   Millwall
749.   22
750.   Hartlepool United

CHESTERFIELD V. GRIMSBY TOWN

751.   3-0 to Chesterfield

752.   Derek Niven

753.   4-4

754.   David Reeves

755.   1997/98 (December 1997)

756.   Division 4

757.   1967/68

758.   Jamie Ward

759.   Mark Allott

760.   True: 1-0 at home and 2-1 away at Chesterfield

CALEB FOLAN

761.   Colman

762.   15

763.   Wigan Athletic

764.   Bradford City

765.   Brentford

766.   1982

767.   Notts County

768.   Leeds United

769.   Republic of Ireland

770.   Striker

2000/2001

771.   York City

772.   Michael Pollitt

773.   Lawrie Dudfield

774.   Luke Beckett

775.   Darlington

776.   25

777.   True

778.   Nicky Law

779.   3rd

780.   Halifax Town

AGAINST WHICH CLUB?

781.   Bristol City

782. **Port Vale**

783. **Norwich City**

784. **Middlesbrough**

785. **Notts County**

786. **Scarborough**

787. **Millwall**

788. **Peterborough United**

789. **Hull City**

790. **West Bromwich Albion**

LEAGUE POSITIONS – 3

791. 1990/91   18th in Division 4

792. 1991/92   13th in Division 4

793. 1992/93   12th in Division 3

794. 1993/94   8th in Division 3

795. 1994/95   3rd in Division 3

796. 1995/96   7th in Division 2

797. 1996/97   10th in Division 2

798. 1997/98   10th in Division 2

799. 1998/99   9th in Division 2

800. 1999/2000   24th in Division 2

NOTES

NOTES

NOTES

NOTES

NOTES

NOTES

OTHER BOOKS BY CHRIS COWLIN:

* Celebrities' Favourite Football Teams

* The British TV Sitcom Quiz Book

* The Cricket Quiz Book

* The Gooners Quiz Book

* The Official Aston Villa Quiz Book

* The Official Birmingham City Quiz Book

* The Official Brentford Quiz Book

* The Official Bristol Rovers Quiz Book

* The Official Burnley Quiz Book

* The Official Bury Quiz Book

* The Official Carlisle United Quiz Book

* The Official Carry On Quiz Book

* The Official Colchester United Quiz Book

* The Official Coventry City Quiz Book

* The Official Doncaster Rovers Quiz Book

* The Official Greenock Morton Quiz Book

* The Official Heart of Midlothian Quiz Book

* The Official Hereford United Quiz Book

* The Official Hull City Quiz Book

* The Official Leicester City Quiz Book

OTHER BOOKS BY CHRIS COWLIN:

* The Official Macclesfield Town Quiz Book

* The Official Norwich City Football Club Quiz

* The Official Notts County Quiz Book

* The Official Peterborough United Quiz Book

* The Official Port Vale Quiz Book

* The Official Rochdale AFC Quiz Book

* The Official Rotherham United Quiz Book

* The Official Shrewsbury Town Quiz Book

* The Official Stockport County Quiz Book

* The Official Watford Football Club Quiz Book

* The Official West Bromwich Albion Quiz Book

* The Official Wolves Quiz Book

* The Official Yeovil Town Quiz Book

* The Reality Television Quiz Book

* The Southend United Quiz Book

* The Sunderland AFC Quiz Book

* The Ultimate Derby County Quiz Book

* The Ultimate Horror Film Quiz Book

* The West Ham United Quiz Book

www.apexpublishing.co.uk